Illustrators:
Jose L. Tapia
Barb Lorseyedi

Editor:
Barbara M. Wally, M.S.

Editorial Project Manager:
Ina Massler Levin, M.A.

Editor in Chief
Sharon Coan, M.S. Ed.

Art Director:
Elayne Roberts

Associate Designer:
Denise Bauer

Cover Artists:
Sue Fullam
Mark Kazlauskas

Product Manager:
Phil Garcia

Imaging:
Ralph Olmedo, Jr.

Publishers:
Rachelle Cracchiolo, M.S. Ed.
Mary Dupuy Smith, M.S. Ed.

Brain Teasers, Puzzles, and Games

K-2

Author:
Carol Monington

Teacher
Created
Materials

Teacher Created Materials, Inc.
P.O. Box 1040
Huntington Beach, CA 92647
ISBN-1-57690-073-8

©1996 Teacher Created Materials, Inc.   Made in U.S.A.

Table of Contents

Introduction

Learning Center Activities for Brain Teasers, Puzzles, and Games presents strategies for solving verbal and non verbal problems and provides practical applications designed to exercise and enhance brain power. These strategies develop analytical and critical thinking skills that apply to all content areas and help children become problem solvers. In addition to critical thinking skills necessary for reading comprehension, vocabulary development, and math, these interesting and challenging hands-on activities provide children with increased confidence in their own abilities.

This book contains over 20 ready-to-assemble learning center activities designed to introduce problem solving strategies, develop visual perception, and provide practical and enjoyable applications of developing skills. Several levels are presented for each activity, allowing the teacher to select or modify the experience for the skills and abilities of the class. Using all of the levels provides further development of a particular skill. The patterns and student pages for each activity are provided in this book. Additional materials, when called for, are inexpensive and readily available. Because the patterns are interchangeable, they may be used in a wide variety of ways.

For each center a list of skills, a student performance objective, a list of the materials needed, and directions for assembling the center are provided. Suggestions for additional centers and new activities to extend the center and provide additional practice and reinforcement of the particular skill are also included. The centers provide individual and/or small group activities for use with students in grades K-2, and are readily adaptable for a variety of age and/or skill levels. These puzzles and games emphasize the following skills:

- sequencing
- visual discernment
- patterning
- fine motor skills
- logic

- comparisons
- creative thinking
- listening comprehension
- oral language development

To keep this valuable resource intact so that it can be used year after year, you may wish to punch holes in the pages and store them in a three-ring binder.

Center Set Up, Use, and Management

Center Set Up

Display: It is best to locate the learning center in a corner of the classroom away from other activity areas and general traffic. If possible, push the center table against a wall under a bulletin board. If a bulletin board is not available, make a display board by cutting the top, bottom, and one side off of a large cardboard box. The remaining three sides form a free standing display board that can be used to display sample projects, directions, and signs. Paint the display board, or cover it with fabric or self adhesive paper. Use map pins, staples, double-sided tape, or self-adhesive Velcro® pieces to attach items to the display board.

Provide enough chairs for the number of students who will use the center, and place a wastebasket under the table.

Signs: Reproduce the center sign and general directions for using the center (pages 6–8) on card stock or oaktag. Use markers, crayons, colored pencils, or paint to decorate the signs. Laminate them for durability.

Materials: Provide a variety of puzzles, purchased, donated, or made from the patterns in this book with subjects related to a classroom theme or puzzles that reinforce concepts.

For younger children, look for puzzles with fewer, larger pieces. As the children's skills increase, add more difficult puzzles.

Use a color or number code on the back of each puzzle piece for organizational purposes, and store the pieces of each puzzle in a self-closing plastic bag or envelope. When the children can put the puzzles together easily, mix the pieces of two or more puzzles together.

Provide boxes, baskets, or other suitable containers of the following general supplies. Number or label the containers, if desired.

- pencils
- scissors
- glue or glue sticks
- crayons, markers, and/or colored pencils

- pre-dampened paper towels
- soft cloth
- grease pencils or dry erase markers
- small plastic bags or envelopes

Additional supplies for specific activities will be added when needed.

Activity Pages: Directions for many of the activities suggest using heavy paper and laminating the activity pages to create durable, reusable activities. The children can write on the surface with a grease pencil or dry erase marker, check their work, then clean the surface with a soft cloth. To substitute for heavy paper, glue copies to oaktag, poster board, or sides cut from cereal boxes before laminating and cutting. If a laminator is not available, self-adhesive laminating sheets or clear, top-loading sheet protectors (available at office supply stores) may be used. You may choose to make individual copies of the activity pages. To provide as much table surface as possible for the students as they work, store the activity pages in large envelopes and place them in a file box under the table, or attach them to the display board.

Center Set Up, Use, and Management *(cont.)*

Other Materials: All of the materials used in the activities are readily available or easily fabricated. You may wish to ask parents to donate buttons, puzzles, pictures, etc. for center use.

Center Use

All of the activities presented in this book are designed to build and enhance critical thinking skills of students in grades K–2. The children follow the directions to solve problems, create products, and/or play games. These activities may be used in any order, depending on the curriculum used in the classroom and the needs of the learners.

Activities in the book are organized in the following sections:

Brain Teasers—activities that require the child to observe, recall specific information, or use deductive reasoning to complete a task

Puzzles—activities in which children manipulate pieces to form coherent patterns or pictures

Games—activities for one or two children which provide an opportunity to apply thinking and reasoning strategies

Each section begins with an overview listing the general skills common to the activities. A specific learning objective which specifies what the learner will be doing and learning is presented for each activity. Specific directions for preparing and presenting each activity include a list of additional materials and a step-by-step guide for creating and decorating the activity cards and/or pieces, instructions for preparing an answer key, and, where needed, student directions.

Following the directions for each activity, the Variations section presents ideas and directions for expanding and modifying the activity. The content or method may be changed to accommodate needs of the learner or to reinforce specific curriculum areas.

Center Management

Provide sufficient time for each student or pair of students to complete the center activities. To insure that each child has an opportunity to use the activity, post a sign-up list near the center. After each child has used the activity, allow individuals to repeat the activity, if they wish to do so. Encourage the children to use the puzzles in the center during their free time. Prepare a chart listing the students in a column on the left side and the title of the activities across the top. Post it on the center display board. As each student completes the activity, either you or the student can place a check in the activity column. You may wish to keep a record of the student's use of the center and performance on the activity in your plan and record book, the student's assignment book, or his or her activity log.

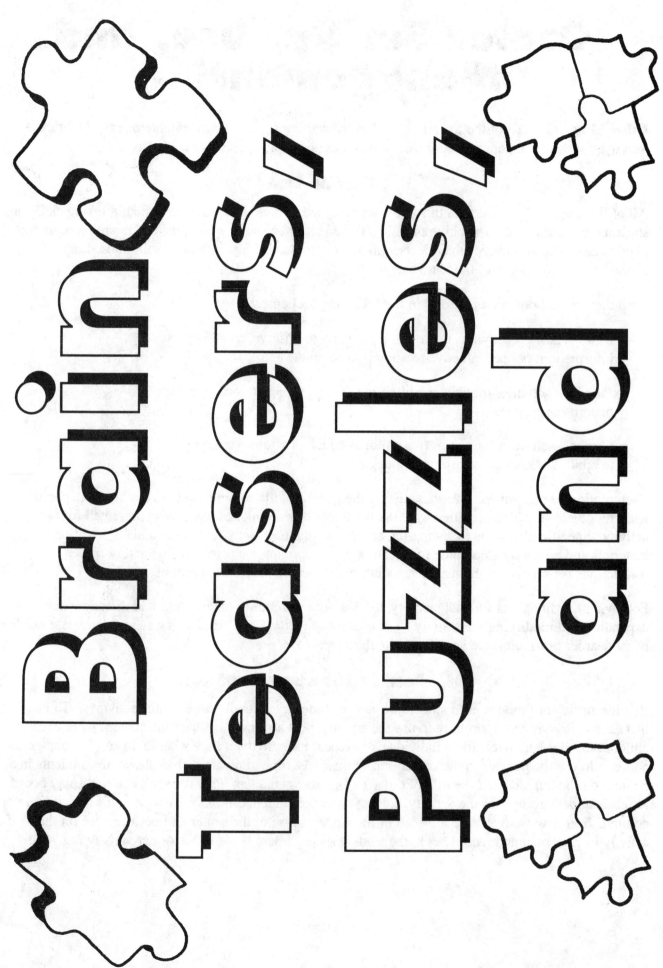

Brain Teasers, Teasers, Puzzles, and

Games Learning Center

Center Directions

1. Listen to directions.

2. Use quiet voices.

3. Gather materials and complete the activity.

4. Cooperate with others in the center.

5. Clean up.

6. Have fun with puzzles.

Brain Teasers Activity Overview

Skills

- pattern recognition
- sequencing
- problem solving
- deductive reasoning
- comparing like and unlike objects
- classification
- following directions

Button Bear

Objective: To follow oral and visual directions to complete a pattern

Materials

general supplies, see page 4

one or more copies of *Corduroy* by Don Freeman (Viking Kestral, 1988)

copies of page 13

variety of real or paper buttons (see patterns on page 14)

tape recorder with ear phones (optional)

story tape of *Corduroy* (optional)

Teacher Preparation: Make copies of the bear pattern on page 13 on card stock or construction paper. Use markers, colored pencils or crayons to add color to one bear for center display and demonstration. Make several copies of page 14, if needed. Assemble the materials for each activity and set them out in attractive, numbered containers, in order of use.

Set the stage by reading *Corduroy*, by Don Freeman, to the entire class during storytime. Discuss Corduroy's lost button and his search for it, with the whole class, asking comprehension questions like these: Why did Corduroy think he needed to find his button? Where did he look for the button? What happened to him? Did Corduroy find his button? Where?

Record the story on cassette for children to listen to individually. (a pre-recorded tape is available from Puffin Story Tapes) Provide a copy of the story so the children can follow along.

Variations

- Pre-cut bears and buttons for less skilled children.
- Put one pair of buttons for each child and several non-matching buttons in a container. Tell the children that Corduroy wants his buttons to match. Have them sort the buttons to find matching buttons, then glue the buttons to the bear.
- Make stuffed bears. Using the pattern on page 13, cut bears from felt, making two for each child. The children staple or glue two bears together, leaving an opening, and gently stuff it with cotton, old nylon hose, or tissue, then staple or glue it closed. Use markers, scraps, buttons, etc. to add features to the bears.
- Continue the story of Corduroy by reading and/or providing copies and tapes of *A Pocket for Corduroy* by Don Freeman (Viking Press, 1978). Provide construction paper squares and instruct the children to give Corduroy a pocket.
- Have the children practice writing their names and/or addresses on a piece of paper to put in Corduroy's new pocket.

Brain Teasers Activity Overview (cont.)

Bears and Buttons

Objective: To develop visual discernment by tracing a line between objects

Materials

    general supplies, see page 4   copies of page 15

Teacher Preparation: Make two copies of page 15 on card stock, or mount the pages on poster board or oaktag. Add color to the illustrations. Use a colored marker to trace the strings on one copy, creating an answer key. Laminate both copies. The children follow the directions, using a grease pencil or dry erase marker to match bears and buttons.

Variation

- Provide individual copies of this activity page. Ask children to color the illustrations and match the bears with their buttons.

Button Bear Maze, A Mazing Bear, Alphabet Maze

Objective: To trace a path through a maze, using visual discernment to decide the correct direction of the line

Materials

    general supplies, see page 4   copies of mazes (pages 16–18)

Teacher Preparation: Make copies of pages 16–18 on card stock, or mount the copies on poster board or oaktag. Use markers, crayons, or colored pencils to add color to the pages, then laminate them. Demonstrate how to complete a maze.

Set out the materials in order of use.

Variations

- Start with simple mazes and work up to more difficult mazes.
- Make individual copies of pages 16–18 for the children to practice on and take home.
- Additional mazes may be found in coloring activity books etc.

Alpha Buttons, A Bee C's, Bears on Parade, Two by Two

Objective: To complete a pattern by supplying missing elements in an alphabetical or numerical sequence

Materials

    general supplies, see page 4   copies of pages 19–22

Teacher Preparation: Make two copies each of pages 19–22 and use colored pencils, markers, or crayons to add color. On one copy, complete the sequence, using a fine line marker. Laminate both pages.

Review or teach writing upper and lower case letters and/or numbers.

Model how to complete a sample sequence of letters.

Variations

- For older or more advanced students, substitute words for alphabetical sequences.
- Have the children practice printing upper and lower case letters.
- Challenge the children to make sequence pages by writing the alphabet and leaving out some letters or numbers. Exchange papers and complete the sequence.
- Change number sequences to reflect higher numbers or counting by 5s or 10s.

Brain Teasers Activity Overview *(cont.)*

What Comes Next?

Objective: To use visual discernment to determine a pattern and predict the next object, letter, or number in the series

Materials

general supplies, see page 4   copies of pages 23–25

Teacher Preparation: Make two copies each of pages 23–25 on card stock, or glue pages to poster board or oak tag. Use crayons, markers, or colored pencils to color the illustrations. Make an answer key by using a fine line marker to complete the series on one set of pages. Laminate all pages.

Variations

- Add color to the buttons on page 23 and provide a container of real or paper buttons. Ask the children to find buttons to match the pictures and use them to cover the pictures before finding a button to complete the series.
- Make individual copies of the pages. Ask the children to predict and draw the next two objects.
- Use real or paper buttons to create more sequences and glue them to poster board. Provide a container of buttons and ask the children to search and sort the buttons in the container to find the next item in the series.

Story Sorting

Objective: To place pictures in a logical sequence which tells a story

Materials

general supplies, see page 4   copies of pages 26–27

Teacher Preparation: Make two copies each of pages 26–27 on card stock, or mount pages on poster board or oaktag. Use markers, crayons, or colored pencils to add color to the story panels. Laminate the pages. Cut one set of pages apart for the children to use, and store each story in a separate envelope. For organizational purposes, color code and/or number all the sequence cards and envelopes. Leave the second set of pages intact to serve as an answer key.

Review story sequences with the children before they use this activity. Remind them to ask, "What happened first?" as they begin their sequence. Demonstrate a simple sequence from a familiar story or fairy tale.

Arrange materials in the center in order of use.

Variations

- For younger children, use shorter, simpler sequences. As their skills develop, make longer sequences.
- When the children have mastered these sequences, mix two or more sets of story cards together. Challenge the children to sort and sequence the stories.
- Have the children create their own stories, using the sequence cards. Make copies of pages 26–27. Instruct the children to select pictures that tell their story, cut them out, and paste them in order to a sheet of construction paper.
- Use pictures from books or magazines, rubber stamps, or stickers to make additional story cards.

Brain Teasers Activity Overview *(cont.)*

How Many Circles? How Many Squares? How Many Triangles?

Objective: To use visual discernment to determine the number of geometric shapes

Materials

general supplies, see page 4   copies of pages 28–30

Teacher Preparation: Make copies of pages 28–30 on card stock, or glue copies to poster board or oaktag. Use markers or colored pencils to add color to the illustrations, and laminate the pages.

Variation

- Use the shapes on pages 28-30 as patterns, and cut matching shapes from construction paper, using a different color for each shape. Challenge the children to assemble the construction paper pieces to match the pages.

Answers:	page 28 8 *circles*	page 29 5 *squares*
	page 30 16 *triangles*	

Analogies

Objective: To compare sets of like and unlike objects based on a common characteristic

Materials

general supplies, see page 4   copies of pages 31–32

Teacher Preparation: Make copies of pages 31–32 on card stock, or glue copies to poster board or oaktag. Use markers or colored pencils to add color to the illustrations, and laminate the pages. Review or teach the concepts of similarity and difference.

Variation

- Create lists of common synonyms and antonyms. Have the children illustrate each pair of words.

Story Time Logic

Objective: To use deductive reasoning to solve a puzzle

Materials

general supplies, see page 4   copies of pages 33–35

Teacher Preparation: Make copies of pages 33–35 on card stock, or glue copies to poster board or oak tag. Use markers or colored pencils to add color to the pages, and laminate them. Demonstrate using the clues to solve the puzzle.

Answers:	page 33 *Maya-3, Jane-2, Sam-1*
	page 34 *Alex-dog, Betty-cat, Chad-fish, Dena-bird*
	page 35 *Ben-chocolate, Chan-strawberry, Maria-vanilla*

Button Bear Pattern

Button Patterns

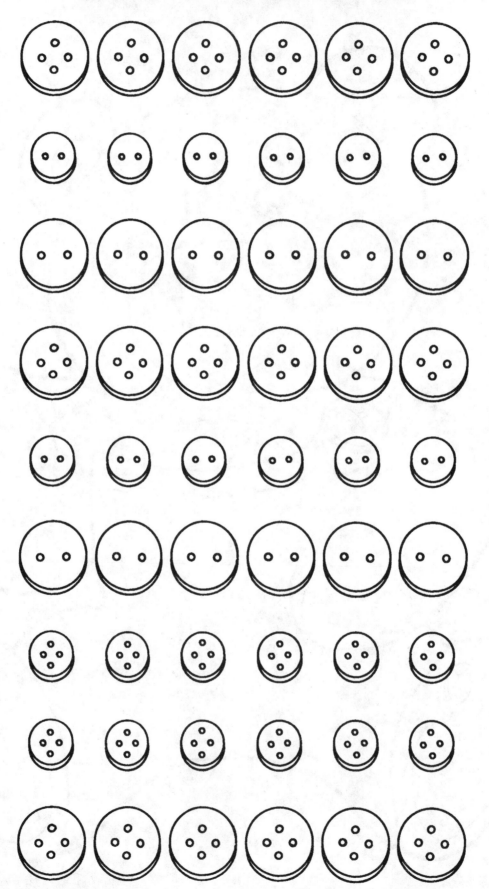

Bears and Buttons

1 2 3 4

_____   _____   _____   _____

Button Bear Maze

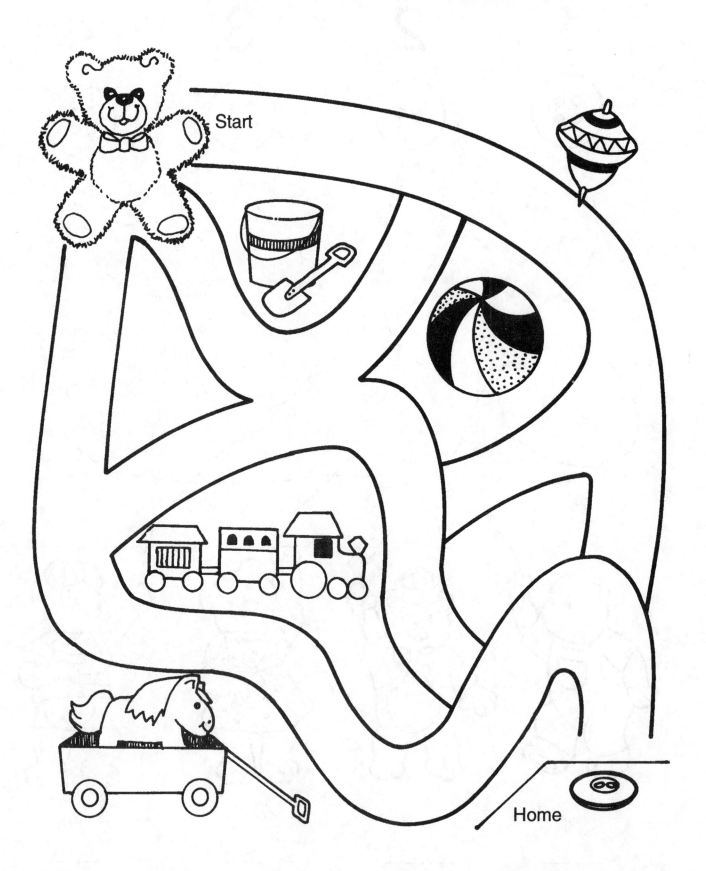

Start

Home

16

A Mazing Bear

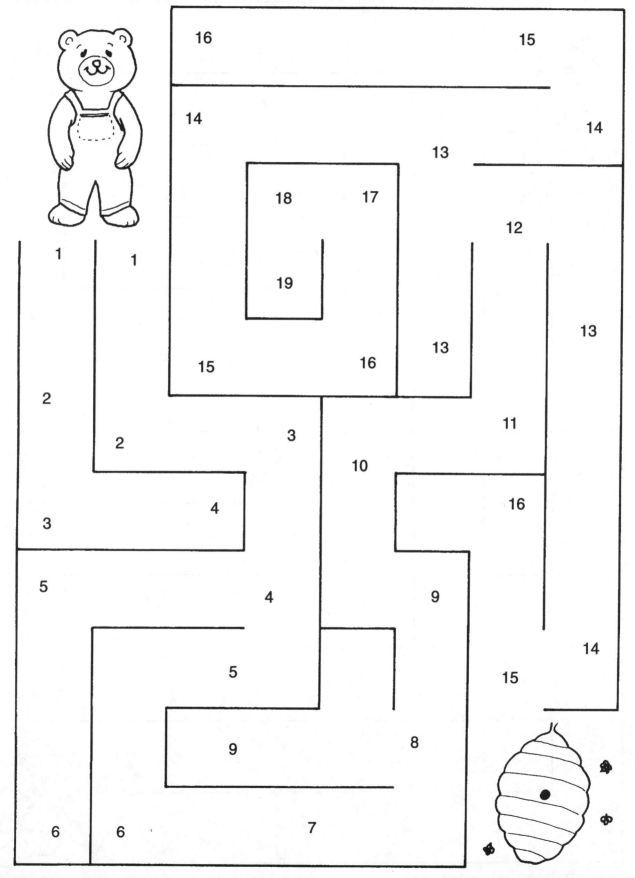

Alphabet Maze

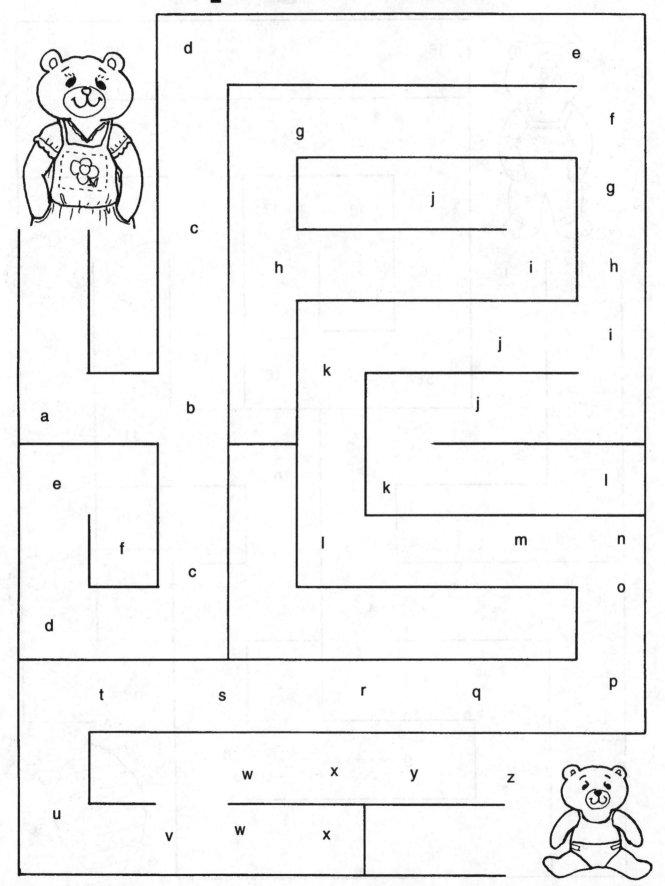

Alpha Buttons

A   B   __   D

E   F   __   H   I   J

__   __   M   N   __   __

Q   __   __   __   U   __

__   __   Z

A Bee C's

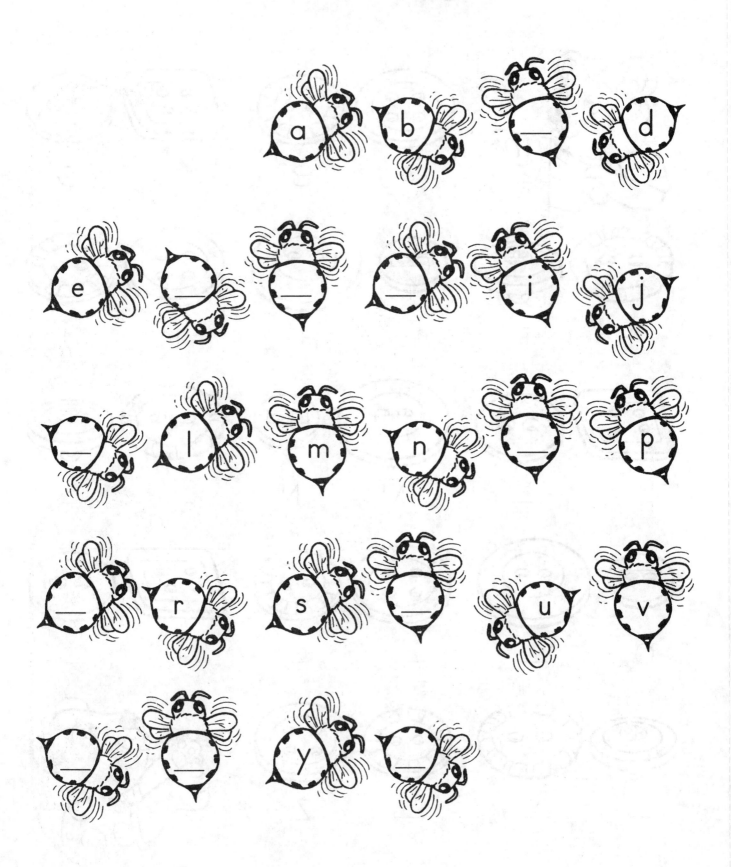

Bears on Parade

The bears are on parade today. Some of them have lost their numbers. Help them get in order by writing the correct number under each one.

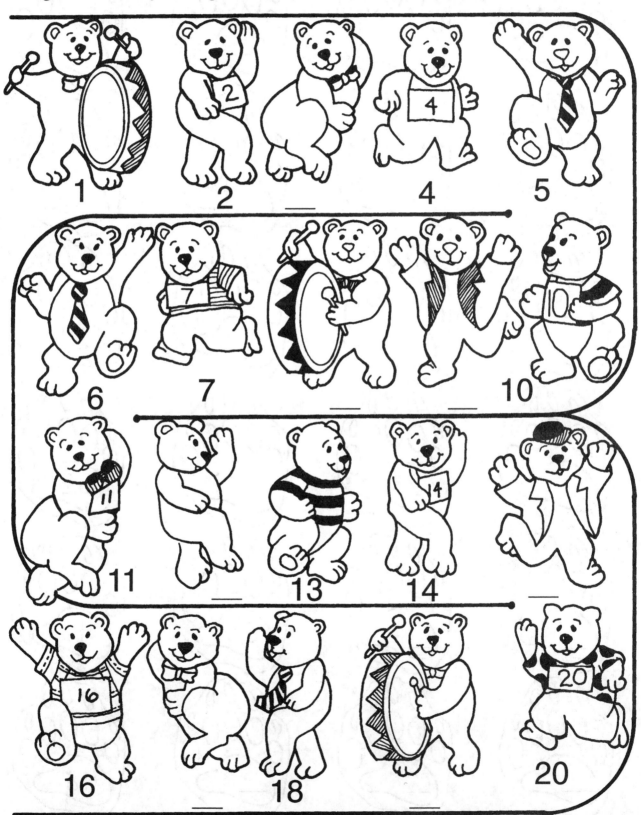

Two by Two

What Comes Next?

Directions

Look at each row of buttons. Decide what comes next and draw it in the space.

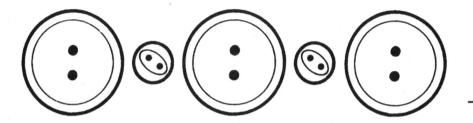

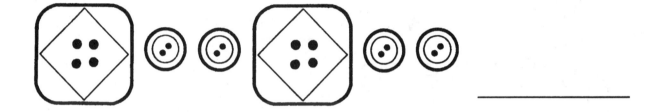

What Comes Next? *(cont.)*

Write the next letter in each series.

1. A B C D E F ____
2. G H I J K L ____
3. M N O P Q R ____
4. S T U V W X ____
5. B C D E F G ____
6. H I J K L M ____
7. N O P Q R S ____
8. T U V W X Y ____
9. Z Y X W V U ____
10. A A B B C C ____
11. C D D C D D ____
12. E F G H E F ____
13. U V U V U V ____
14. Q R S Q R S ____

What Comes Next? *(cont.)*

Write the next number in each series.

A. 1 2 3 4 5 6 7 8 _____

B. 2 4 6 8 10 12 14 16 _____

C. 1 3 5 7 9 11 13 15 _____

D. 5 10 15 20 25 30 35 40 _____

E. 10 20 30 40 50 60 70 80 _____

F. 9 8 7 6 5 4 3 2 _____

G. 1 1 2 2 3 3 4 4 5 5 _____

H. 1 4 7 10 13 16 _____

I. 1 2 3 1 2 3 1 2 _____

J. 1 2 2 1 2 2 1 2 _____

K. 1 2 2 3 3 3 4 4 4 _____

L. 1 1 2 1 1 3 1 1 2 _____

M. 1 2 3 4 1 2 3 4 _____

N. 1 5 1 10 1 15 1 20 1 _____

O. 1 2 1 2 1 2 _____

Story Sorting

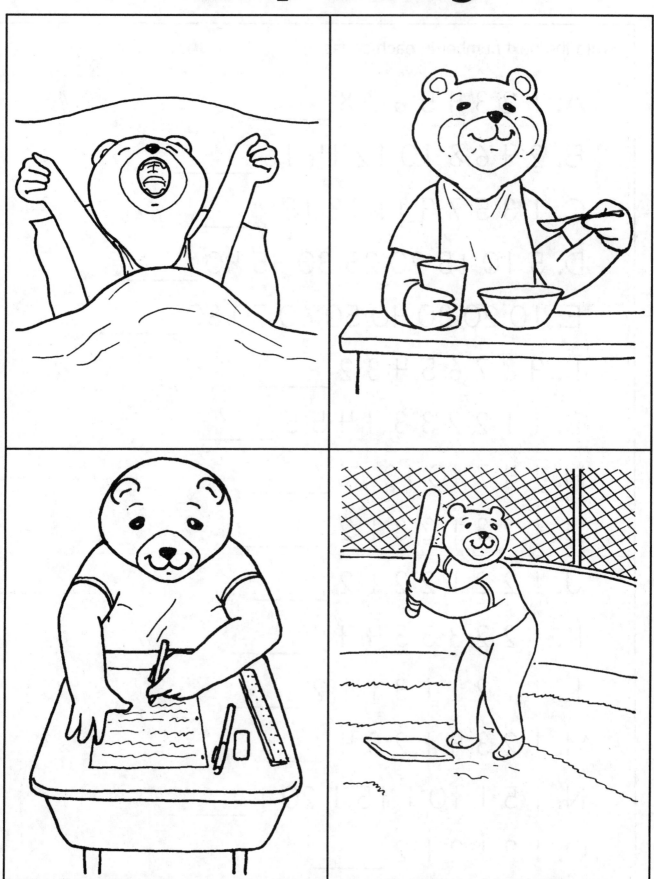

Story Sorting (cont.)

How Many Circles?

How many circles are in the picture? Use a different colored marker to trace each one, then count them.

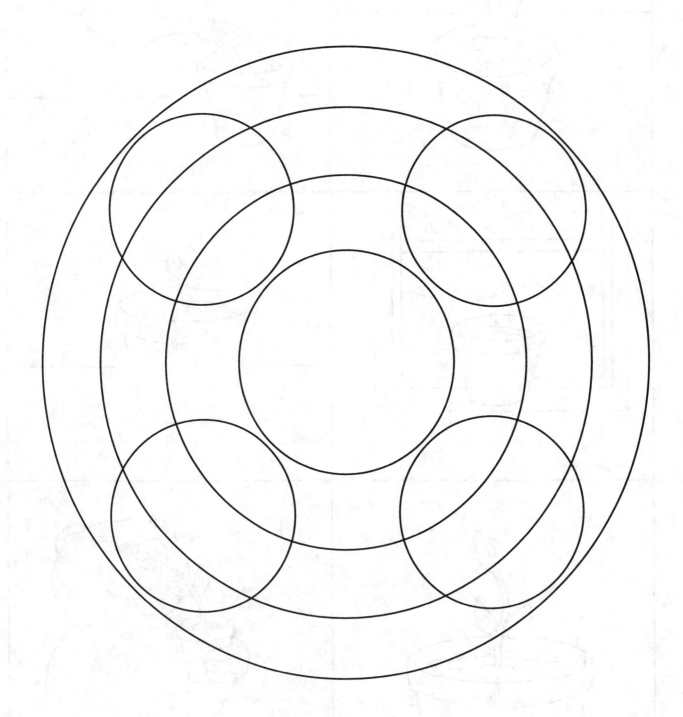

How Many Squares?

How many squares are in the picture? Use a different colored marker to trace each one, then count them.

How Many Triangles?

How many triangles are in the picture? Use a different colored marker to trace each one, then count them.

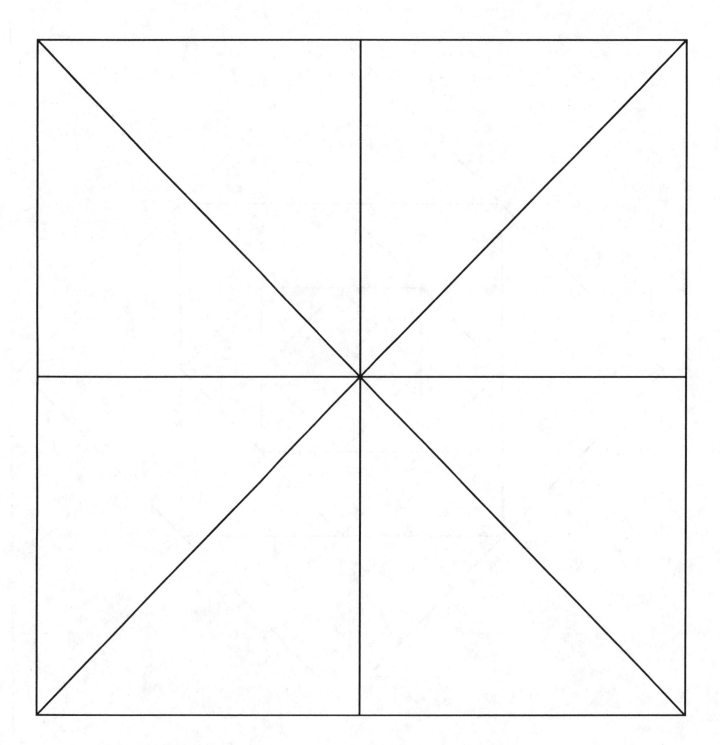

30

Analogies

Look at the pictures. Decide which one completes the comparison. Write the number of the picture in the space.

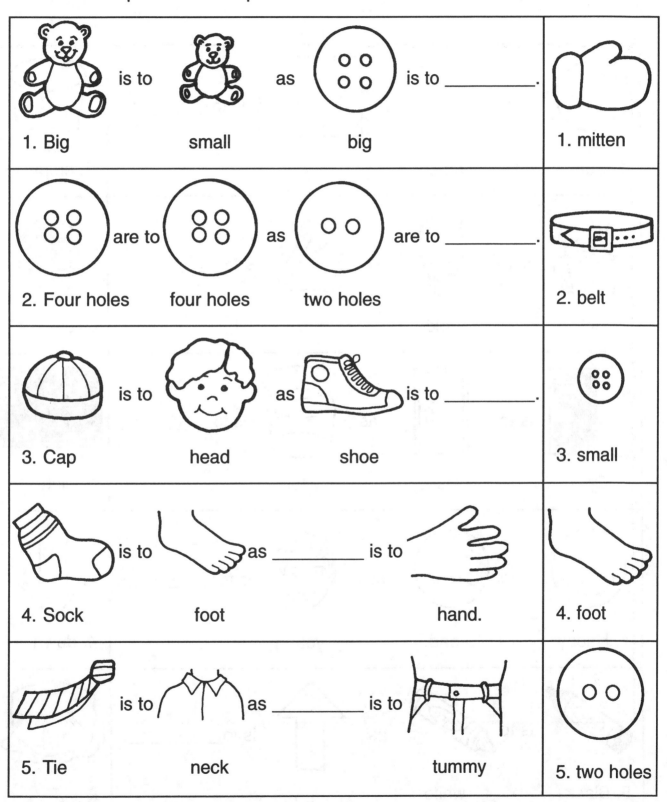

1. Big   small   big   1. mitten

2. Four holes   four holes   two holes   2. belt

3. Cap   head   shoe   3. small

4. Sock   foot   hand.   4. foot

5. Tie   neck   tummy   5. two holes

Analogies (cont.)

Look at the pictures. Decide which one completes the comparison. Write the number of the picture in the space.

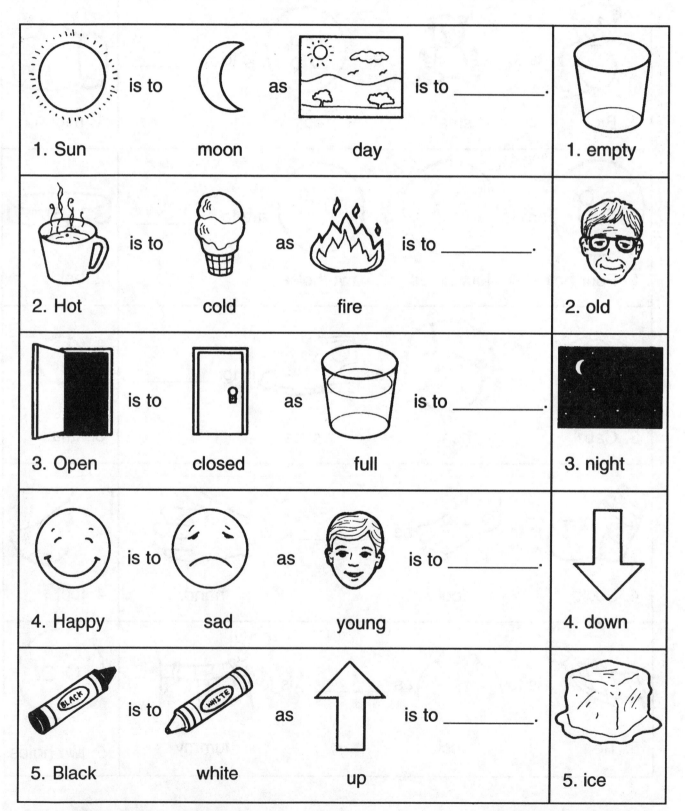

1. Sun	moon	day	____.	1. empty
2. Hot	cold	fire	____.	2. old
3. Open	closed	full	____.	3. night
4. Happy	sad	young	____.	4. down
5. Black	white	up	____.	5. ice

Story Time Logic

Goldilocks has invited three friends, Maya, Jane, and Sam to a tea party. Each friend has brought one bear. The bears are different sizes. Can you use the clues to figure out which bear came with which friend? Draw a line to connect each bear to its owner.

> 1. Jane's bear is not the biggest or the smallest.
> 2. Maya's bear is bigger than Sam's bear.

Story Time Logic *(cont.)*

Alex, Betty, Chad, and Dena each brought a pet to the pet show. Each child has a different kind of pet. Can you use the clues to figure out which pet belongs to which child?

1. Dena's pet does not have fur.
2. Chad's pet lives in the water.
3. Betty's pet likes to climb trees.

Alex

Betty

Chad

Dena

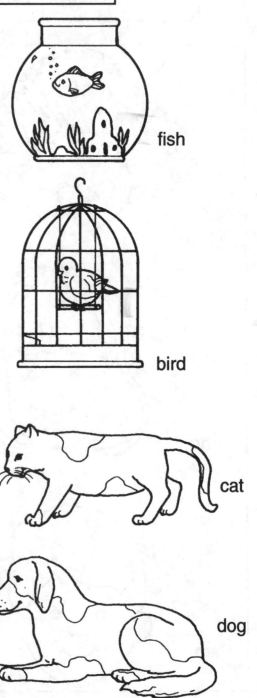

fish

bird

cat

dog

Story Time Logic *(cont.)*

At the ice cream shop, Ben, Chan, and Maria each one bought an ice cream cone. Each cone is a different flavor and has a different number of scoops. Can you use the clues to match each child to his or her ice cream cone? Draw a line from the child to the cone.

1. Ben and Maria do not like strawberries.
2. The strawberry cone is the smallest.
3. The vanilla cone has two scoops of ice cream.
4. Ben has the most ice cream.

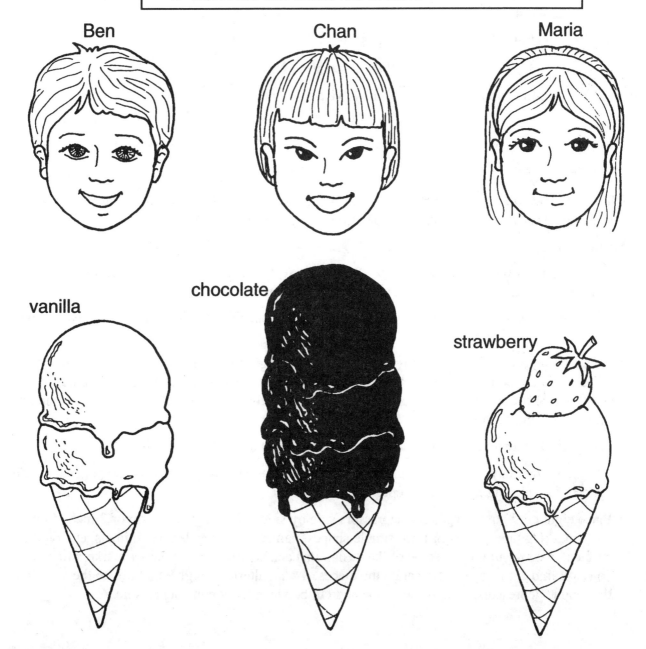

Ben   Chan   Maria

vanilla   chocolate   strawberry

Puzzles Activity Overview

Skills

- sequencing
- letter and number recognition
- eye/hand coordination
- visual discernment
- fine motor skills
- sorting/classification
- thinking/reasoning strategies
- creativity/imagination

Bear Puzzle, Teddy Bear Puzzles

Objective: To assemble pieces to form a complete picture, by matching colors, shapes, and patterns

Materials

general supplies, see page 4

copies of pages 41–43

construction paper

jigsaw puzzles

Teacher Preparation: Make copies of pages 41–43 for each child.

Puzzle Pattern

Objective: To follow directions to create and solve a puzzle

Materials

general supplies, see page 4

copies of pages 40–43

craft sticks or tongue depressors

picture file

Teacher Preparation: Color and cut one set of the patterns on pages 40–42 for demonstration and center display. Make copies of the puzzle pattern on page 43 for each child.

Variations

- Make copies of the blank puzzle, page 43, on card stock. The children draw their own pictures, or write their names, letters, or numbers on the puzzle, and cut along the lines.

- The children can trace their hands or feet on the blank puzzle, add color, and cut along the puzzle lines.

- As an alternative, provide a supply of pictures from magazines, old work sheets, etc. Have the child select a picture from the picture file, glue it to card stock or poster board, add color if desired, and cut into puzzle pieces. If you use page 43 for this activity, instruct the children to glue the picture to the back of the blank puzzle.

- Have the children exchange puzzles they have made and solve them.

- Older children may write a letter to a friend or family member on a blank puzzle page and cut it apart before placing it in an envelope.

- Place eight craft sticks or tongue depressors side by side (touching) on a strip of 2 inch (5 cm) wide masking tape. Draw or trace simple shapes, names, numbers, letters, animals, etc. on the surface, making sure to get some of the design on each stick. Use crayons or markers to add color. Remove the tape and separate the pieces. As an alternative, glue pictures to the surface of the tongue depressors. Remove the tape and cut between the tongue depressors.

Puzzles Activity Overview (cont.)

Take Apart Teddy Bear

Objective: To identify parts of a whole and assemble them to create a recognizable form

Materials

general supplies, see page 4

pattern sheet, page 44

scraps of fabric, paper, or buttons for decorating, if desired

self-adhesive Velcro® tabs

Teacher Preparation: Make one copy of page 44 for each child. Make, decorate, and laminate one copy of page 44 for demonstration and center display. Use heavy paper like card stock, poster board, or oaktag to make it durable.

Variations

- Prepare several bears in different colors. Mix the pieces. Instruct children to make complete bears by matching the colors.

- Pre-cut bear parts for younger or less skilled children.

- Punch holes where the Velcro® would go and use paper brads to make a jointed, movable bear.

- Pre-cut several copies of the bear. Store the pieces in envelopes, labeled by part name. Ask the children to select the appropriate parts to assemble a bear.

- Working in pairs, have one child lie down on the floor on a large sheet of craft paper. The second child draws around the first child. The children change places. Each child decorates and cuts out his or her outline. Assemble the pieces the same way as the teddy bear.

Dot-to-Dot Bears

Objective: To complete a pattern by drawing a line connecting letters or numbers in a sequence

Materials

general supplies, see page 4

copies of dot-to-dot pictures (pages 45–48)

grease pencil, crayon, or dry erase marker

soft cloth

Teacher Preparation: Make reusable center copies by decorating and laminating one copy of each activity. Provide grease pencils or dry erase markers and a soft cloth for erasing the laminated pages. Complete and decorate one set of activity pages to use as an answer key (laminate, if desired). Teach or review the alphabet/numbers. Check for visual recognition of upper case letters/numbers. For younger children, model reciting the alphabet/numbers in order as you connect the dots.

Variations

- Make copies of pages 45–48 for each child.

- Change the activity sheets in any of the following ways: reverse the alphabetical or numeric order, select a section of the alphabet like K-U instead of A-K, begin the number sequence with a two digit number, change the numbers to show skip counting by 2, 5, or 10.

Puzzles Activity Overview *(cont.)*

Teddy Bear Lacing Cards

Objective: To outline or complete a pattern using a lace in the correct sequence

Materials

general supplies, see page 4

copies of pages 49–50

single hole punch

scissors

lacing material like shoe laces, yarn, or ribbon

masking tape

Teacher Preparation: Prepare copies of pages 49–50 on card stock, oaktag, or poster board. Use markers, crayons or colored pencils to add color to the pictures. Letter or number sequences may be added with a fine line marker, if desired. Laminate the cards for durability, then cut around each shape. With a single hole punch, make holes as indicated on each picture.

If yarn or ribbon will be used for lacing, thread one picture to measure the appropriate length for laces. Cut several laces. Wrap one end of each piece of yarn or ribbon with tape to prevent fraying.

Use the lacing card to demonstrate how to lace before children use this center.

Variations

- For younger or less skilled children, make very basic, simple cards with only a few holes.

- Prepare several different cards for the children to use for practice. Use the dot-to-dot bear pictures, pages 45–48, or other patterns from this book. Decorate and laminate the pictures before punching holes.

- Have the children create their own lacing cards. Make copies of each pattern on card stock. For younger or less skilled children, pre-cut and punch the cards. Have the children decorate and lace their bears.

- Experiment with different lacing patterns. Older or more advanced students may use a second lace, reversing the in-and-out order to create a different pattern.

- Make hanging pockets to hold the children's work. Provide a paper plate for each child. Cut additional paper plates in half. Punch holes at one inch (2.54 cm) intervals around the whole and half plates. Have the children decorate the face of the whole plate and the back of the half plate. Place the half plate face down on the whole plate, aligning the holes. Use yarn or ribbon to lace the plates together, beginning and ending at the top of the whole plate. Tie the ends together to make a hanging loop.

Hide and Go Seek; Button, Button

Objective: To find and count objects hidden in a picture

Materials

general supplies, see page 4

copies of pages 51–52

Teacher Preparation: Make two copies each of pages 51–52 on card stock, or glue paper copies to poster board or oaktag. Use colored pencils, markers or crayons to add color to the illustrations. With a fine line marker, complete the activity on one copy to serve as an answer key. Laminate both pages.

Puzzles Activity Overview (cont.)

Word Buttons

Objective: To solve a word puzzle by selecting parts of the whole

Materials

general supplies, see page 4   copies of pages 53–54

Teacher Preparation: Make two copies of pages 53–54 on card stock, or glue paper copies to poster board or oaktag. Use colored pencils, markers or crayons to add color to the buttons and illustrations. Complete the activity on one copy to serve as an answer key. Laminate both pages.

> **Answers:** page 53 *shirt, jacket, overalls;* page 54 *doctor, fireman, teacher, teddy bear*

Variations

- Change the letter sequences to make more word puzzles, substituting the children's vocabulary, number, or color words, or a short phrase.

- Make larger buttons or wheels, and insert additional letters between the letters of the word.

Bear Mobiles

Objective To assemble like and/or unlike objects to create a mobile

Materials

paper plates   dental floss, fishing line, or string
hole punch   paper clips
construction paper   copies of pages 55–56

Teacher Preparation: Copy, decorate, and laminate directions. Make copies of page 56 on card stock or colored construction paper. Cut the centers from paper plates, leaving a one inch (2.54 cm) ring. Prepare one mobile for demonstration and center display. Demonstrate how to assemble the mobile. Balance is important. If children will be using materials of different sizes and weights, show them how to adjust placement so that the mobile will hang straight.

Assemble all patterns and materials and place them in the center in order of use.

Variations

- Pre-cut the shapes if necessary for younger children.

- Use wire or plastic clothes hangers in place of plates.

Whose Bear Is It?

Objective: To assemble pieces to form puzzle pairs by matching characteristics

Materials

general supplies, see page 4   copies of page 57

Teacher Preparation: Copy, color, and laminate puzzle pairs. Cut out the pairs. Demonstrate to the children how to look for the characteristics and how to match the puzzle pieces.

Variations

- Cut out pictures from magazines and let children find the similar and different characteristics in them.

- Use the puzzle pairs as patterns and create your own puzzles using copies of photos of the children in your class.

Bear Puzzle

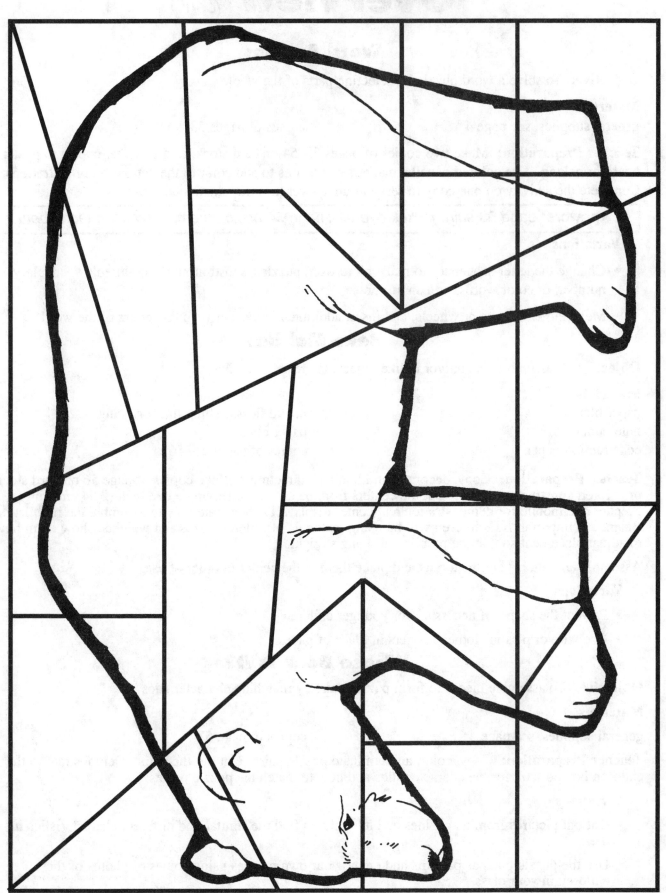

Teddy Bear Puzzle

Teddy Bear Puzzle

Puzzle Pattern

Take Apart Bear

Dot-to-Dot Letter Bear

Dot-to-Dot Letter Bear

Dot-to-Dot Number Bear

Dot-to-Dot Number Bear

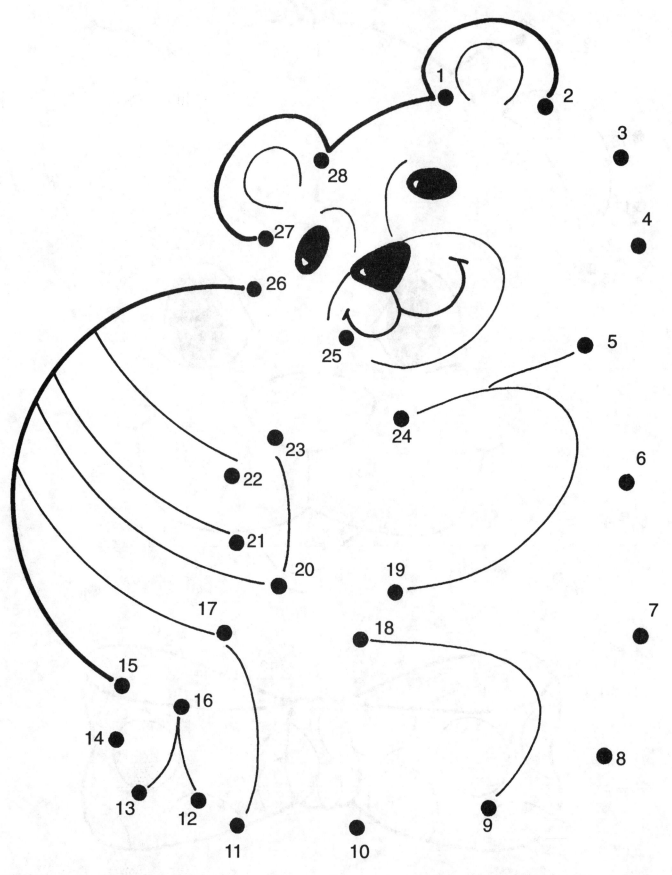

Teddy Bear Lacing Card

Teddy Bear Lacing Card

Hide and Go Seek

The teddy bears are playing hide and seek in their room. How many of them can you find?

Button, Button

How many buttons are in the picture? Draw a circle around each one you find and count them all. Remember to look for the lost buttons!

52

Word Buttons

Directions

1. Draw a circle around every other letter on each button, beginning at the 1. The first one is done for you.

2. Write the letters in order on the blanks to learn where each button belongs.

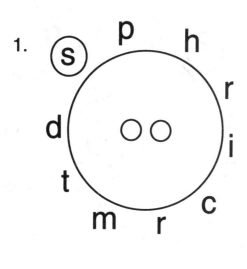

1.

___ ___ ___ ___ ___ ___

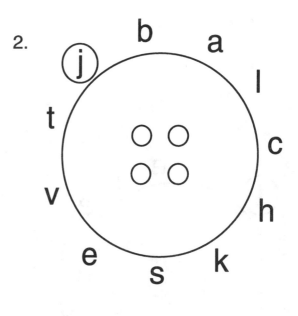

2.

___ ___ ___ ___ ___ ___

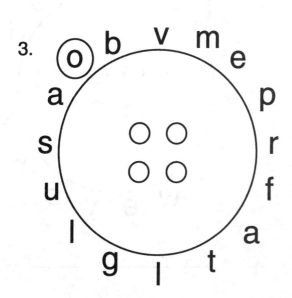

3.

___ ___ ___ ___ ___ ___ ___

Word Buttons *(cont.)*

Directions

1. Draw a circle around every other letter on each button, beginning at the 1. The first one is done for you.

2. Write the letters in order on the blanks to learn where each button belongs.

1.

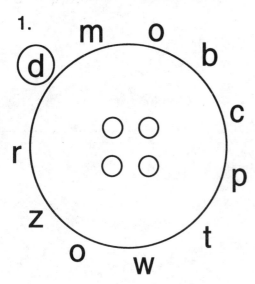

___ ___ ___ ___ ___ ___

2.

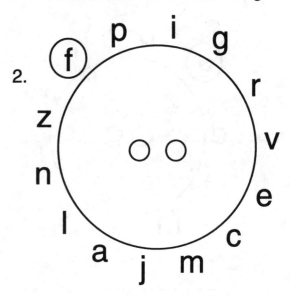

___ ___ ___ ___ ___ ___

3.

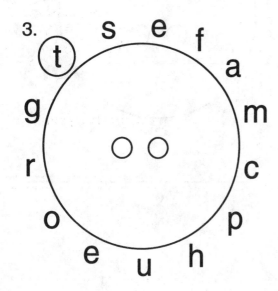

___ ___ ___ ___ ___ ___ ___ ___

4.

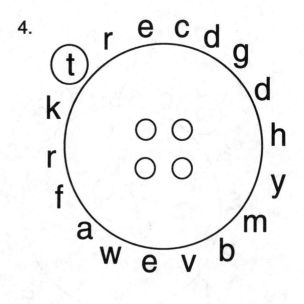

___ ___ ___ ___ ___

Bear Mobiles

Directions

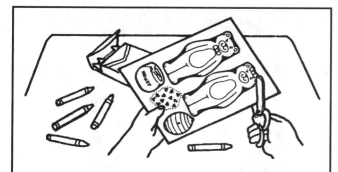

1. Color the bears and cut them out.

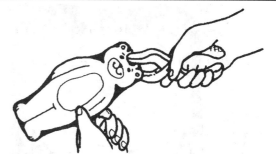

2. Punch a hole in the top of each bear.

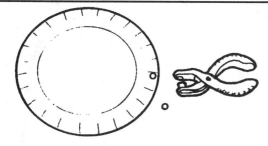

3. Punch a hole in the plate rim for each bear.

4. Tie a knot in one end of a piece of string.

5. Thread the string through the hole in a bear.

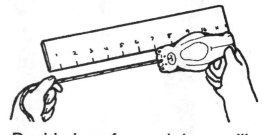

6. Decide how far each bear will hang from the plate, and tie a knot in the string.

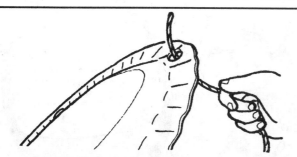

7. Thread the string through a hole in the plate rim.

8. Gather the tops of the strings together and tie them to a paper clip.

Bear Mobiles *(cont.)*

Patterns

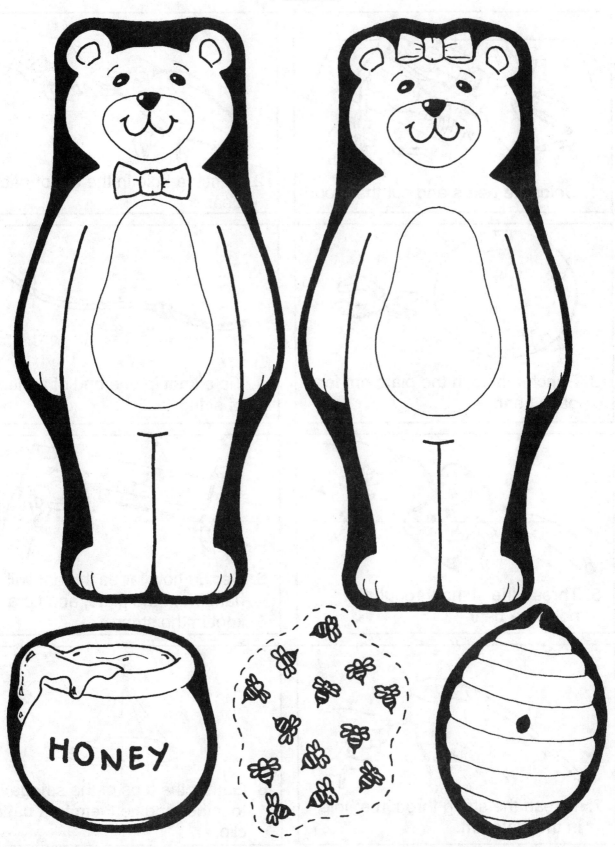

HONEY

Whose Bear Is It?

Can you find the clues hidden in the pictures and use them to figure out which bear belongs to which child?

Tina

Susan

Nick

Juan

Jade

Games Activity Overview

Skills

- visual discernment
- spatial relationships
- volume
- estimation

- memory building
- matching
- creating sets
- thinking and reasoning strategies

- eye/hand coordination
- size/color discrimination
- problem solving skills
- sorting/classification

Button Box

Objective: To sort objects into sets based on observation of characteristics

Materials

general supplies, see page 4   copies of pages 14 and 62

egg carton, small containers, or self-closing plastic bags

Teacher Preparation: Reproduce the pattern on page 14 and glue it to poster board or oak tag. Use markers, colored pencils, or crayons to create sets of buttons in four different colors, or make the copies on different colors of paper. Cut out the buttons and sort them in separate containers, bags, or sections of the egg carton. Color the button sorting sheet on page 62 to match the sets of buttons. If students will be sorting by other characteristics, like two holes and four holes, add these details. Laminate the pages, if desired. Demonstrate sorting to the class.

Ask the children to sort the buttons by color, size and/or by shape.

Variations

- Provide sets of six buttons of the same style in four graduated sizes. Pair the children and instruct them to take turns wearing a blindfold and using touch to sort the buttons by size.

- Glue a variety of buttons to a piece of poster board. Remove the flaps from small envelopes and glue one under each button as a pocket. Tell the children to drop the matching buttons into the appropriate pocket.

- This activity may be used for math. The buttons and button box serve as manipulatives for explaining and comparing sets and can be used as counters for addition and subtraction problems. Vary the number of buttons in each color to create equal and/or unequal sets. Have the children sort the buttons and compare the resulting sets.

- Demonstrate simple addition problems by combining sets. For example, given a set of 4 red, 3 green and 2 yellow buttons, the child first counts and records all buttons, then counts the buttons of each color. Ask for a combination, like how many red and yellow buttons? The child groups the red and yellow buttons and counts them.

- For hands-on subtraction practice, the child pairs the members of the sets. Unpaired buttons represent the answer.

- Write the problems and prepare containers of buttons to match the problems.

Games Activity Overview *(cont.)*

The Guessing Game

Objective: To estimate the number of objects in a given space

Materials

general supplies, see page 4

assorted real or paper buttons

sorting box (page 62) or container for sorting

baby food jar, spice jar, or small self-sealing plastic bag

copies of page 63

Teacher Preparation: Make a copy of page 63 on card stock, or glue the page to poster board or oaktag. Use crayons, markers, or colored pencils to add color and decorate the page and laminate it. Put a quantity of similar size buttons of various colors in a clear container or a small self-sealing plastic bag. Provide two or three different samples, varying the number and/or size of the buttons.

Set the materials out in the center in the order of use. The children follow the directions to estimate (guess), then check themselves by counting the objects.

Variations

- Count the number of buttons and record answers on a copy of the record sheet to be used as an answer key.
- Replace the buttons with other small objects, like marbles, jelly beans, gummy bears, etc. Ask the children to compare the amounts.
- Select containers in different sizes and/or shapes.
- Ask the children to predict how many buttons there are of each color, then count them by color as above.

Goldie's Locks and Keys

Objective: To match related objects based on a given characteristic

Materials

general supplies, see page 4

copies of pages 64–66

Teacher Preparation: Copy pages 64–66 on heavy paper, like oaktag, poster board, or card stock. Color and decorate the game board as desired. Add various colors to the locks and keys, making matching pairs. Laminate the pages for durability, if desired. Cut apart the locks and keys, and store them in a small envelope. Post them on the center display, or, if the game board and pieces are stored in a large envelope, glue the directions to the outside of the envelope.

Variations

- This game may be played by two children. The child with the most matches wins the game.
- Change the game cards to reflect other paired items, like upper and lowercase letters, numbers, numerals and number words, colors and color words, etc.

Games Activity Overview *(cont.)*

Color Dominoes

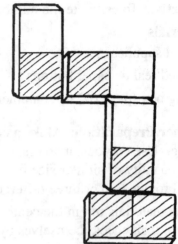

Objective: To create a pattern by matching like characteristics of game pieces

Teacher Preparation: Make copies of pages 67–68 on card stock, or glue the pages to poster board or oaktag. Use markers, crayons, or colored pencils to add the designated colors to each card. Laminate the page, if desired, and cut out the cards. Demonstrate building patterns by matching the colors. Store dominoes in an envelope or self-closing plastic bag.

Variations

- Provide one or more sets of standard dominoes for the children to play with.
- Create new domino games by changing the patterns on the cards to letters, number patterns, numerals, animal pictures, etc. Use rubber stamps or stickers for the illustrations.
- Have the children make sets of dominoes. Provide copies of pages 67–68, and tell the children to glue the pages to construction paper, color the dominoes, and cut them apart. Put the finished cards in an envelope or small plastic bag.

Bear Card Game

Objective To play a game by matching numbers to create a set

Materials

general supplies, see page 4   copies of pages 69–71

Teacher Preparation: Make two copies each of pages 70–71, using different colored paper for each set of pages. Use markers and/or colored pencils to highlight the numbers and illustrations on each set of the cards. Glue the pages to card stock, poster board, or oaktag, and laminate them before cutting the cards apart. Make one copy of the directions on page 69 on card stock, or mount the page on poster board or oaktag. Highlight and decorate the directions with colored pencils, markers, or crayons, and display them in the center. If necessary, demonstrate and explain the game to the children.

Variations

- For older children, make two additional sets of cards in different colors. Tell them that they must match the numbers on four cards to make a set.
- Use the teddy bear playing cards to play other card games, like "Old Maid," "Crazy 8s," etc.
- Individual children may use the playing cards to practice matching and sorting by color and/or numbers or ordering numbers in ascending and descending order.
- Have each child make his or her own set of cards. Provide copies of pages 70–71, and tell the children to glue the pages to construction paper, color the pictures, and cut out the cards. Put the finished cards in an envelope or small plastic bag.

Games Activity Overview *(cont.)*

Teddy Bear Paper Dolls

Objective: To follow directions to create a set of paper dolls to be used as props in story telling

Materials

general supplies, see page 4   copies of pages 72–76

Teacher Preparation: Make copies of page 72 on card stock, or glue pages to poster board or oaktag. Use markers, crayons, or colored pencils to add color to one set of paper dolls. Laminate the page and cut out the dolls. Make copies of pages 73–76. Add color to one set of clothing with crayons, markers, or colored pencils. Cut out the clothing.

Demonstrate dressing the dolls for the children. Emphasize the importance of cutting around the tabs on the clothing.

Have diagram and materials set out in order of use.

Variations

- Pre-cut dolls and clothes for younger or less skilled children.
- Provide several sets of teddy bear paper dolls. Use the patterns on pages 73–76, copy ideas from teddy bear history books, coloring books, teddy bear magazines, etc., or purchase sets at bookstores, doll shops and school supply stores.
- Hang up a clothesline and have the children clothespin the laminated paper doll clothes on the clothesline. Another option is to use real doll clothes or real people clothes.

Secret Button Patterns

Objective: To use deductive reasoning to determine a pattern, based on correct and incorrect responses

Materials

general supplies, see page 4   real or paper buttons

copies of pages 77–78

Teacher Preparation: Make copies of pages 77–78. Use markers, crayons, or colored pencils to add color to the game boards and highlight the directions with a fine line marker. Laminate the pages and cut out the two game boards. Fold the pattern maker's board as indicated. Provide 24 similar size buttons in each of two colors.

Variations

- Ask individual students to use the button sets and game board to find how many possible patterns there are. (15)
- Increase the color choice to three colors and play the game. How many combinations are now possible?

Teddy Bear Finger Puppets

Objective: To follow oral and written instructions to create a puppet to be used in story telling

Materials

general supplies, see page 4   copies of page 80 for each child

Teacher Preparation: Make one copy of page 79 and copies of pages 79-80 for each child. Use markers, crayons, or colored pencils to decorate the directions and one copy of the patterns. Laminate the pages, cut out the puppets and assemble them to use for demonstration and center display. Arrange materials in the center in order of use.

Button Box

Place the buttons in the box according to their color.

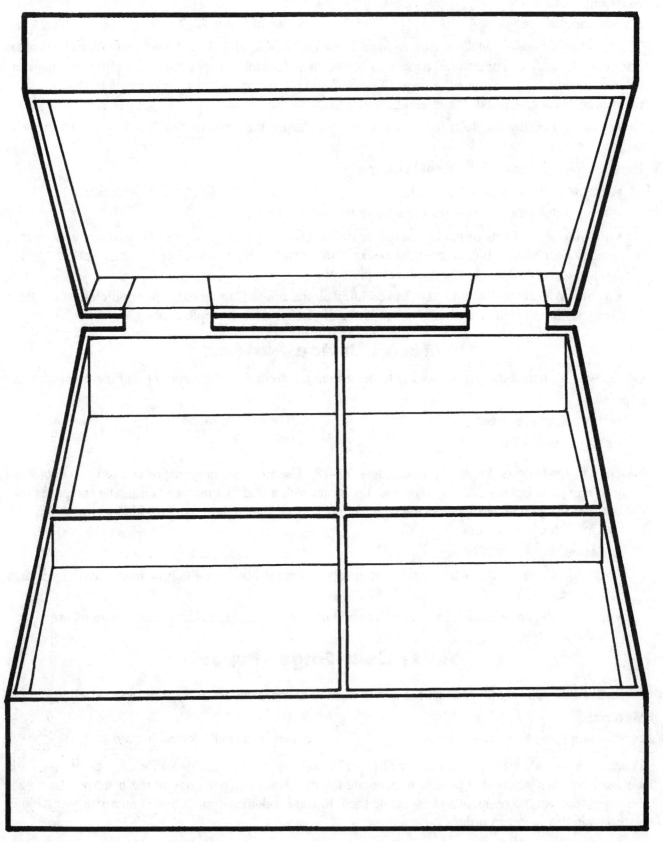

62

The Guessing Game

Can you guess how many buttons are in the container? Follow the directions to see how close you can come.

1. Look at the container. Decide how many buttons you think are in it.

2. Write your guess in the **?** Space on the record sheet.

3. Count the buttons. Write the number of buttons in the Total space.

4. Compare the two numbers. How close were you?

5. Put the buttons back in the container.

6. Use the same directions to guess the number of each button color.

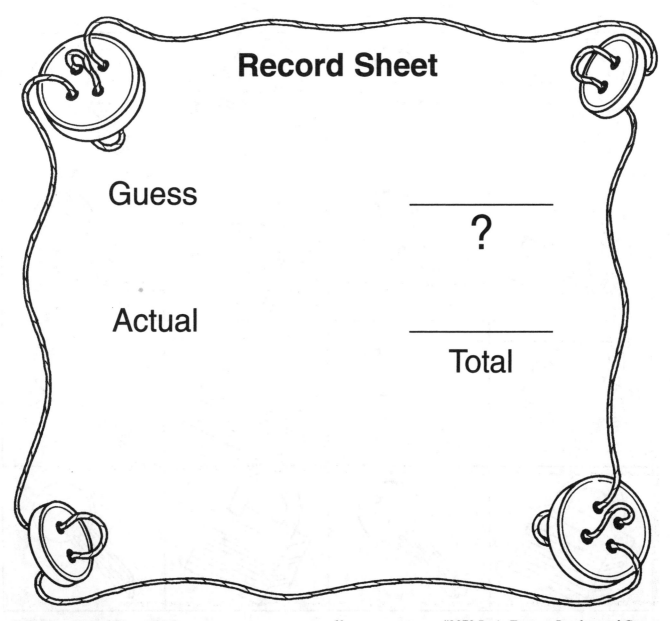

Record Sheet

Guess   _____

                           ?

Actual   _____

                        Total

Goldie's Locks and Keys

Goldie's Locks and Keys (cont.)

Goldie's Locks and Keys *(cont.)*

Directions

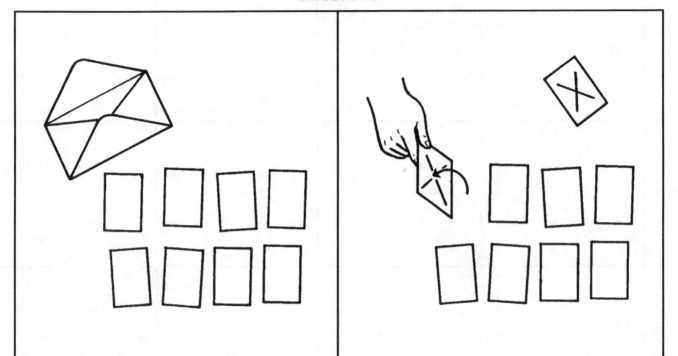

1. Take the game pieces from the envelope and place them face down on the playing board.

2. Turn over two cards. If they match, remove them from the board.

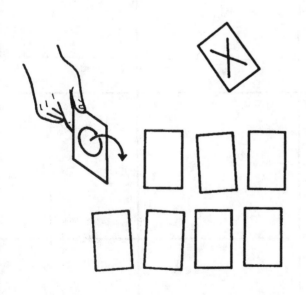

3. If they do not match, put them back on the board, face down.

4. Mix up the pieces and play again.

Color Dominoes

Directions (for 2 players)

1. Turn the dominoes face down on the table and mix them up.

2. Each player draws 5 dominoes.

3. The first player puts one of his or her dominoes face up in the center of the table. The second player tries to match one of his or her dominoes to the domino on the table. If a match is not possible, draw another domino.

4. Continue playing until all the dominoes are gone or there are no more matches. Play again.

red	red	red
red	blue	yellow

red	red	red
green	orange	purple

Color Dominoes *(cont.)*

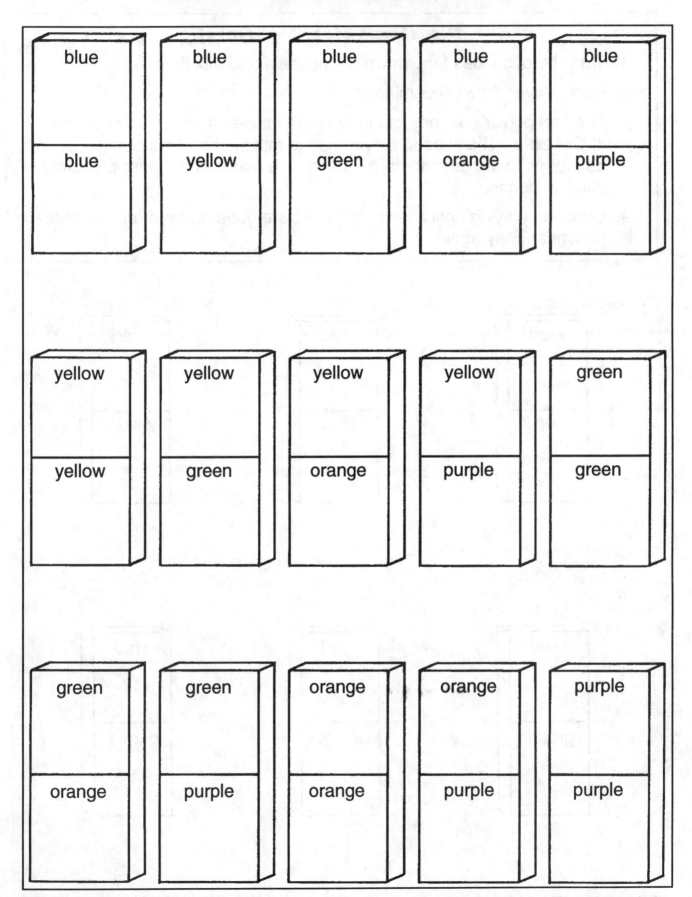

Bear Card Game

Go Honey Directions

1. Shuffle the cards

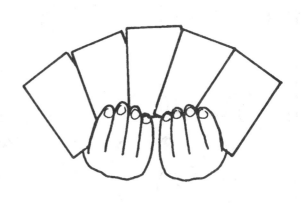

2. Each player draws 5 cards.

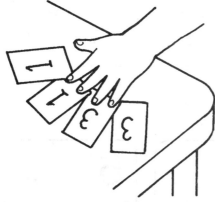

3. If the player has matching cards, he or she puts them on the table.

4. The first player asks the second player for a number. If the second player has that card, he or she gives it to the first player, and the first player asks for another number.

5. If the second player does not have the number, he or she says "Go Honey." The first player draws a card from the pile, and the second player can now ask for a number.

6. The game ends when one player has no more cards in his or her hand.

Bear Card Game (cont.)

Teddy Bear Playing Cards

Bear Card Game *(cont.)*

Teddy Bear Playing Cards *(cont.)*

7

7

8

8

9

9

10

10

11

11

12

12

Teddy Bear Paper Dolls

Directions

1. Gather the necessary materials.

2. Color and decorate dolls.

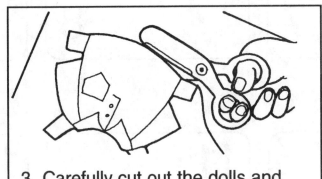

3. Carefully cut out the dolls and clothing.

4. Free play with paper dolls.

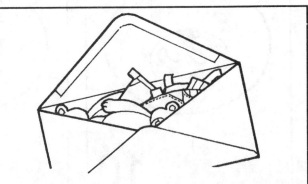

5. Put in envelope to take home.

Teddy Bear Paper Doll (cont.)

Patterns

Teddy Bear Paper Doll (cont.)

Patterns (cont.)

Teddy Bear Paper Doll *(cont.)*

Patterns *(cont.)*

Teddy Bear Paper Dolls (cont.)

Patterns (cont.)

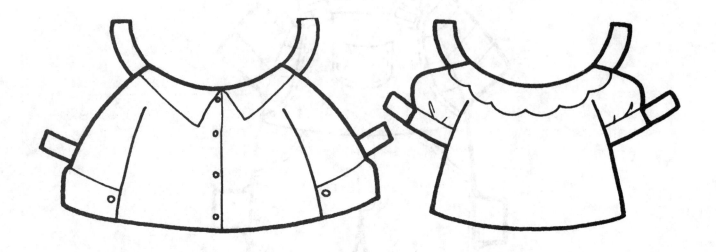

Secret Button Patterns

Directions
(Game for 2 players)

1. Decide who will be the pattern maker first. 	2. The pattern maker arranges four buttons on the pattern board. Do not let the other person see the pattern! 
3. The player then arranges a pattern on his or her game card. 	4. The pattern maker compares the player's card to his own. If a player's button is in the right order, put a small button at the top of the column on the player's card. 
5. The player creates a new pattern, including information learned in the previous turn. 	6. The pattern maker checks the new pattern, and marks it. 
7. Play continues until the patterns match. 	8. Change cards and play again. 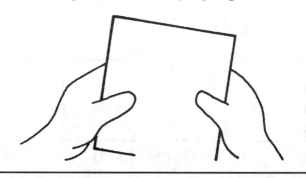

Secret Button Patterns *(cont.)*

1.			
2.			
3.			
4.			
5.			
6.			
7.			
8.			

Game Board

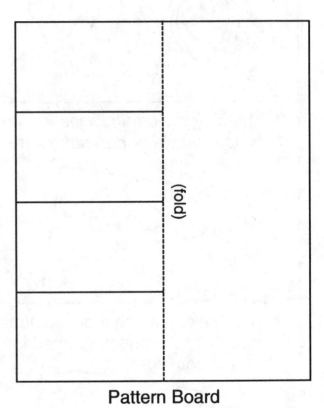

Pattern Board

Teddy Finger Puppets

Directions

1. Take a pattern page.

2. Color and decorate finger puppets.

3. Cut them out.

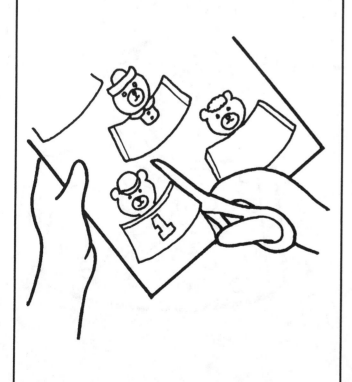

4. Glue tabs together as shown in the diagram.

GLUE

Teddy Finger Puppets *(cont.)*